ABC
I Like Me!

by Nancy Carlson

Macmillan
McGraw-Hill

**This book is dedicated to
the memory of my Grandma Dorothy.
She was a *great* teller of jokes!**

The *McGraw·Hill* Companies

**Macmillan
McGraw-Hill**

Macmillan/McGraw-Hill
A Division of The McGraw-Hill Companies
Two Penn Plaza, New York, NY 10121

This edition is printed in arrangement with Puffin Books, a division of Penguin Young
Readers Group, a member of Penguin Group (USA) Inc., 345 Hudson Street, New York,
NY 10014.

ISBN 0-02-197820-4/Pre-K

2 3 4 5 6 7 8 9 [109] 10 09 08 07

Feeling good about me is as easy as ABC!

I am **A**wesome,

Brave, and

Cheerful.

I have big Dreams,

and I like to Explore.

I am a good Friend.

I love to Giggle

and be Happy.

I have a great

Imagination.

I can Jump and Juggle.

I am **K**ind.

I am a good **L**eader.

Sometimes, I make Mistakes.

And sometimes, I'm Noisy!

I love to play **O**utside.

I try to be Polite.

I like **Q**uiet times

so I can Read.

I am good at **Sharing**.

I am Talented!

Look at me—I'm Unique!

I try to eat all my Vegetables.

I like to make **Wishes.**

XXX OOO!

Yawn . . . I need a good

night's sleep, so tomorrow . . .

I can Zoom on!